to:
Audrey &
Stella,
Hope you enjoy
my book...
'Dave Huddleston

CALL *of the* CHILD II

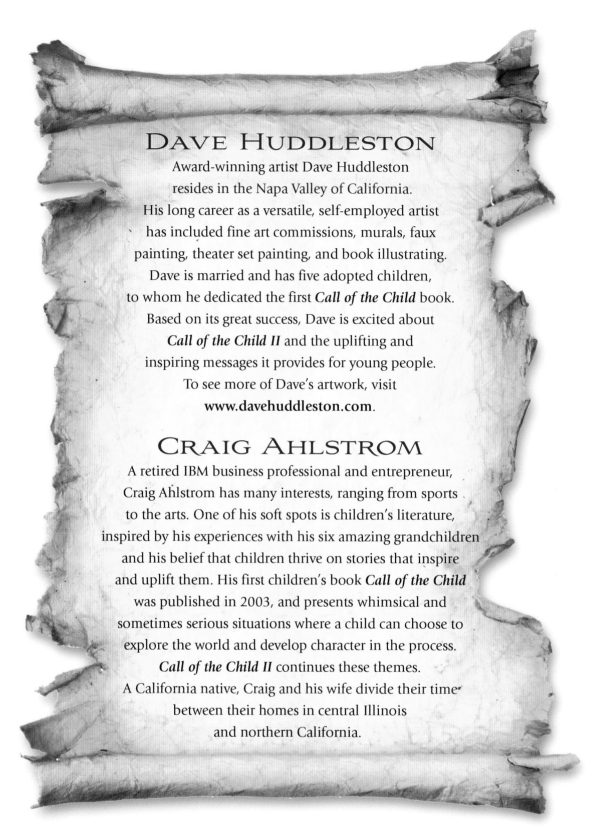

DAVE HUDDLESTON

Award-winning artist Dave Huddleston
resides in the Napa Valley of California.
His long career as a versatile, self-employed artist
has included fine art commissions, murals, faux
painting, theater set painting, and book illustrating.
Dave is married and has five adopted children,
to whom he dedicated the first *Call of the Child* book.
Based on its great success, Dave is excited about
Call of the Child II and the uplifting and
inspiring messages it provides for young people.
To see more of Dave's artwork, visit
www.davehuddleston.com.

CRAIG AHLSTROM

A retired IBM business professional and entrepreneur,
Craig Ahlstrom has many interests, ranging from sports
to the arts. One of his soft spots is children's literature,
inspired by his experiences with his six amazing grandchildren
and his belief that children thrive on stories that inspire
and uplift them. His first children's book *Call of the Child*
was published in 2003, and presents whimsical and
sometimes serious situations where a child can choose to
explore the world and develop character in the process.
Call of the Child II continues these themes.
A California native, Craig and his wife divide their time
between their homes in central Illinois
and northern California.

ISBN-13: 978-0-9719202-1-7

Copyright © Perfect World Publishing, 2013

Poems © 2013 by Craig Ahlstrom and Dave Huddleston
Illustrations © 2013 by Dave Huddleston
Graphic Design by Morning Star Design, Springfield, Illinois
Printed in the United States of America by Versa Press

CALL *of the* CHILD II

Created by

Craig Ahlstrom *and* Dave Huddleston

SPIRIT

Rise up, be brave, young soldiers of life,
Prepare to greet the day.
Accept each challenge with courage,
Lead others and show the way.

Success will be your great reward,
Worth more than precious gold.
If you live your life with passion,
Life's treasures will unfold.

Chart your craft to far off lands,
Remember you're not alone.
Inspire yourself and others,
To greater heights unknown.

WISDOM

Ever feel you're better,
Than 'whooo' you are today?
Knowing something great in you,
Is surely on its way?

What you see and what you'll get
Aren't always the same thing.
The wise old owl wasn't born that way,
It took a lot of learning.

The person you will finally be,
Is one you've not yet met.
Just remember, thankfully,
God's not finished with you yet.

$\mathcal{B}$ᴇ $\mathcal{Y}$ᴏᴜʀsᴇʟꜰ

Chameleons change their color,
For them a trait that's good.
By camouflaging who they are,
They avoid becoming food.

People also change their looks,
With others to blend in.
Becoming who they're really not,
For friends they hope to win.

Show yourself for who you are,
Embrace the real you.
Take pride in your uniqueness,
And to yourself be true.

ACCEPTANCE

My friends don't look the same as me,
I've decided that's ok.
They're all unique individuals,
We've been designed that way.

I figure we're all creatures,
Of this same great Earth we share.
Accepting other's differences,
To me seems only fair.

A person's real beauty,
Is not something we can see.
A heart with love and kindness,
Is what matters most to me.

LOYALTY

Loyal friends are hard to find,
Like rare and precious gems.
And when they come into your life,
You'll learn to treasure them.

When choosing friends be careful,
They'll help shape who you will be.
Look for traits that you respect,
Like compassion and honesty.

Nourish your friendships often,
With love and kindness, too.
Remember to always treat them,
As you would like them to treat you.

Focus

The twists and turns that each life takes,
Are often like a maze.
Sometimes the road is clear, but then,
At times a foggy haze.

Don't lose yourself along the way,
Of warning signs beware.
Curves and potholes line this path,
To trap you like a snare.

Keep your road map handy,
That's the wisdom you've received.
One whose focus stays on track,
Will seldom be deceived.

ADVENTUROUS

Diamonds, pearls, and treasure chests,
That spill of precious gold.
These are yours, young buccaneers,
To share with others bold.

Cast away from your safe shore,
Into uninviting waters.
The ocean deep will share its wealth,
With only brave sons and daughters.

A true north compass needle,
Will guide you toward its secret.
The real treasure, you will find,
Is a true adventurer's spirit.

PERSPECTIVE

The smallest, softest raindrops,
In numbers fill the sea.
From a lonesome, buried acorn,
Will rise a mighty tree.

When doubt creeps in and you feel small,
The feelings hurt your heart.
But look around at all that's great,
See where it got its start.

A simple, small beginning,
Is where we all have been.
Believe you are a conqueror,
And you will surely win.

HOPE

Don't judge a book by its cover,
A saying that is true.
It means you have special qualities,
Which are uniquely you.

Look beyond the surface,
See the princess in the girl.
Know those hardened clamshells,
Can embrace a cultured pearl.

A caterpillar worms along,
Not knowing its full story,
Until the morphing butterfly,
Spreads its wings in glory.

Will Power

You may think you can't do much,
If you're weak and frail.
But toughness comes from deep inside,
Believe you will not fail.

Some will test your strength of will,
And think you'll come up short.
But you won't blink when challenged,
Nothing of the sort.

Doubt may whisper to your heart,
"You may not make it through it!"
But your confidence and faith reply,
"Just trust your heart and do it!"

RESOLVE

Late at night when others sleep,
You chase a flickering glow.
Silently glide through marshy bog,
Through a swamp of indigo.

Some would say it's a scary place,
With hungry snakes and hippos.
Your oarsman steers you skillfully,
Dodging rocks and large mosquitoes.

When you're not sure of where to go,
Afraid you've lost your way.
Use resolve to persevere,
And you will find your way.

RIDE

When you feel there's less of you,
Than you would like to be.
When you know there's more to you,
Than others really see.

Remember those who count you out,
Don't know the strength you hide.
That core of great potential,
Won't always stay inside.

Know there is no other,
Exactly as you are.
A one-of-a-kind creation,
Shining as the morning star.

Effort

Striving for and hoarding,
All the riches that you can.
Becomes a stress-filled burden,
For the materialistic man.

Material wealth can come and go,
Much too easily.
And always where your treasure is,
Your heart will also be.

Success will not be measured,
By the riches you possess,
But by the effort you've put in,
That shows you've done your best.

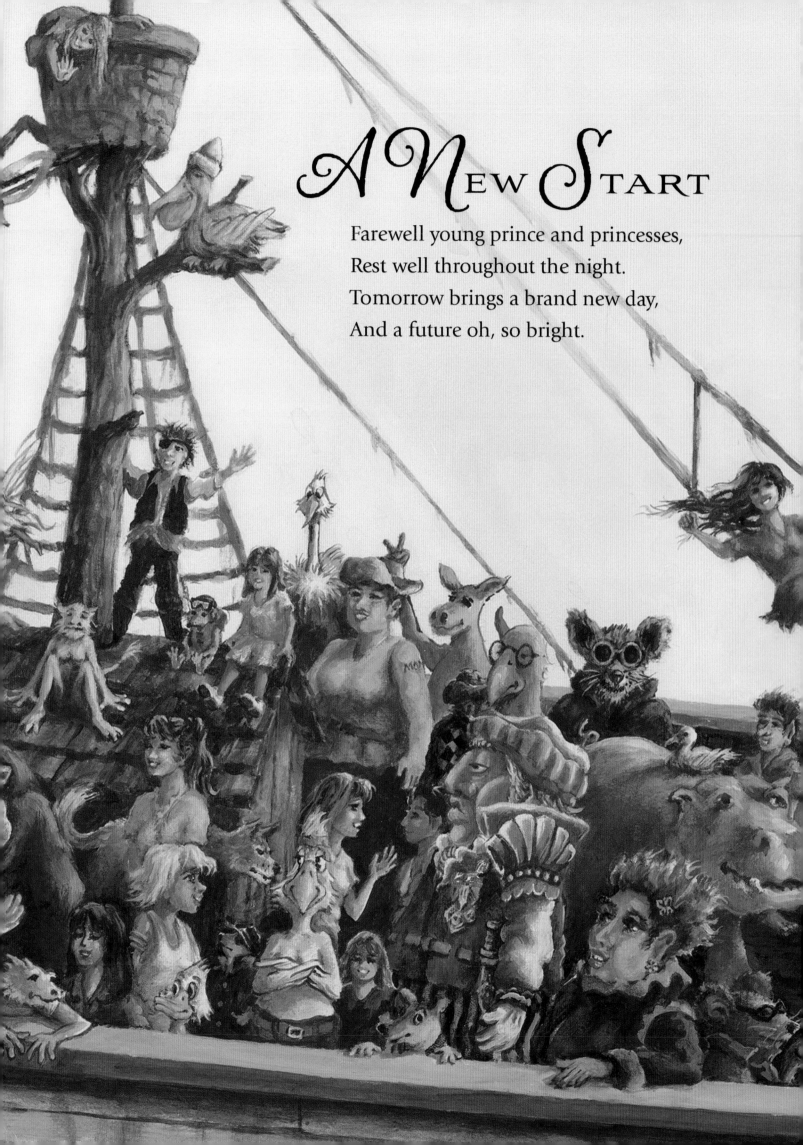

A New Start

Farewell young prince and princesses,
Rest well throughout the night.
Tomorrow brings a brand new day,
And a future oh, so bright.

The End